BOOK 5

FOUR STAR

SIGHT READING AND EAR TESTS

DAILY EXERCISES FOR PIANO STUDENTS

BY BORIS BERLIN AND ANDREW MARKOW

Series Editor

SCOTT McBRIDE SMITH

National Library of Canada Cataloguing in Publication Data

Berlin, Boris, 1907-
    Four star sight reading and ear tests [music]

ISBN 0-88797-789-8 (Introductory level). —
ISBN 0-88797-791-X (bk. 1). — ISBN 0-88797-793-6 (bk. 2)
ISBN 0-88797-795-2 (bk. 3). — ISBN 0-88797-797-9 (bk. 4)
ISBN 0-88797-799-5 (bk. 5). — ISBN 0-88797-801-0 (bk. 6)
ISBN 0-88797-803-7 (bk. 7). — ISBN 0-88797-805-3 (bk. 8)
ISBN 0-88797-807-X (bk. 9). — ISBN 0-88797-809-6 (bk. 10)

1. Piano — Studies and exercises. 2. Ear training.
3. Sight-reading (Music) I. Markow, Andrew, 1942- II. Title.

MT236.B473 2002   786.2'142'076   C2002-900877-8

FREDERICK
HARRIS
MUSIC

ISBN-10: 0-88797-799-5
ISBN-13: 978-0-88797-799-2

PREFACE

The ability to read music at sight at the piano is an important skill for all musicians. As piano students work toward fluency in sight reading, develop aural proficiency, and gain a practical knowledge of theory, they will build a foundation of musicianship that will help them to understand music throughout their lives.

Are some pianists naturally better sight readers than others? Not really. But some recognize patterns on the printed page more readily. Such students use their **visual learning skills**. Other students use their natural **tactile sense** to move around the keyboard quickly. Still others have an innate **aural ability** to hear both melody and harmony with only a glance at the score. Some students may also apply **analytical skills** learned from a study of theory to understand form and content.

The goal of the *Four Star* series is to develop each of these skills and abilities in equal measure. In the process of completing the *Four Star* series, students will improve not only their sight-reading skills but also their proficiency in learning and memorizing music. They will also expand their coordination of eyes, ears, and hands, and their powers of concentration and observation. As a result, *Four Star* students will develop confidence in themselves and in their musical abilities and performance.

Each of the 11 *Four Star* volumes contains daily exercises in sight reading and ear training and builds a foundation for an analytical approach to sight reading music, using examples taken from the standard repertoire. (Some excerpts have been modified by the authors for pedagogical reasons.)

Completion of each *Four Star* book effectively prepares students for the corresponding level of examination systems, including:
- RCM Examinations
- Certificate of Merit (Music Teachers Association of California)
- National Guild of Piano Teachers
- most MTNA curriculums

In order to develop students' reading and overall musical abilities more fully, the authors have chosen to exceed the requirements of most examination systems.

HOW TO USE THIS BOOK

The purpose of the *Four Star* series is to provide daily exercises in sight reading and ear training for students to practice at home, as well as tests to be given by the teacher at the lesson. Best results will be obtained through daily student practice and consistent monitoring and testing at the lesson by the teacher.

SIGHT READING AND RHYTHM

The daily sight-reading and rhythm exercises are intended for students to do by themselves. There are five exercises per week, each including a short piece and clapping rhythm. The rhythms are grouped together following the sight-reading piece for the fifth day.

Suggestions on how to proceed are found on p. 4. It is useful for teachers to review these at the lesson, as well as the reference section on Musical Elements and Patterns in This Volume (pp. 6 and 7).

Drills for reading chords and 18th-century ornaments have been introduced at this level. Teachers may begin working on these drills at the lesson (for example, see p. 11) . As the student progresses, these drills may be assigned as part of home practice. Examples from the Supplementary Material (pp. 62–64) should be included with the regular tests at the lesson.

EAR TRAINING

Ear-training exercises can be found following the sight-reading and rhythm drills. These, too, are designed to be practiced by the student alone, as assigned by the teacher.

Suggestions on how to proceed are found on p. 5.

TESTS

Tests are found beginning on p. 48. These are designed to be given by the teacher at the lesson at the conclusion of the corresponding week's work. Supplementary material may be found in the series *Melody Playback/Singback* and *Rhythm Clapback/Singback* by Boris Berlin and Andrew Markow.

SUGGESTIONS FOR PRACTICING SIGHT READING AND RHYTHM

Before playing the piece:

1) Look at the *key signature*, important notes and patterns, and the opening and closing notes to determine the tonality.
2) Look at the *time signature*, *note values*, and *rhythmic patterns*, and decide on the best way to count.
3) Look for any *rhythmic problems*, and clap or tap the rhythm while counting.
4) Notice the *tempo* indication, if any. Do not play *andante*, *moderato*, *lento*, etc. too fast.
   It is usually better to play *allegretto*, *allegro*, *presto*, etc. a little slower in order to play accurately.

T.F. Dunhill

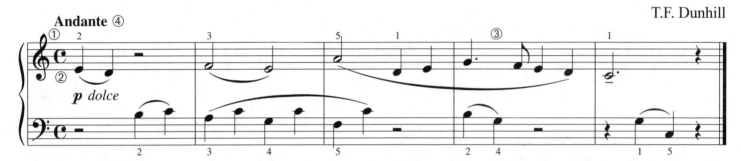

① The key signature has no sharps or flats. The opening note is E and the closing notes are G and C. The closing cadence is V–I in C major. Therefore, the key (tonality) is C major.

② The time signature is **c** (four ♩ notes in a measure). The note values are 𝅗𝅥, 𝅘𝅥., ♩, and ♪; and the rhythmic patterns are: 𝅘𝅥 𝅘𝅥 𝅘𝅥 𝅘𝅥 | 𝅗𝅥 𝅗𝅥 ‖ 𝅗𝅥 𝅘𝅥 𝅘𝅥 | 𝅘𝅥. ♪♪ 𝅘𝅥 ‖ 𝅘𝅥 𝅘𝅥 – | ♩ 𝅘𝅥 𝅘𝅥 ♩ ‖

③ Be careful of the dotted quarter followed by an eighth (𝅘𝅥. ♪).

④ The tempo is *Andante*, which means at a walking pace.

EXERCISES FOR CLAPPING OR TAPPING RHYTHMIC PATTERNS

To prepare for the Daily Rhythms, clap or tap each of the following rhythmic patterns several times.

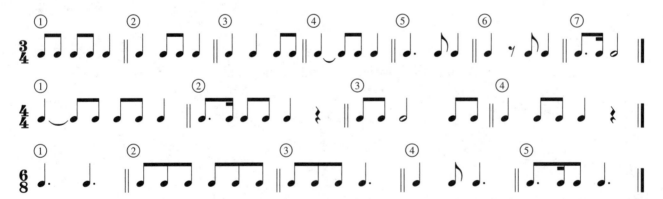

Now clap or tap each of the following combinations of rhythmic patterns taken from the Daily Rhythms in this book.

SUGGESTIONS FOR PRACTICING EAR TRAINING

RHYTHM

To improve rhythm skills and help memorize the rhythm of a melody by ear, the student should:

1) name the time signature;
2) look at the combination of note values that form the rhythm;
3) play or sing (on one note) the rhythm of the melody while reading the music;
4) sing, clap, or tap the rhythm while looking at the music; and finally,
5) sing, clap, or tap the rhythm **from memory**.

Each step may be repeated several times.

INTERVALS

An *interval* is the distance between two notes. Learn to recognize the color and character of the *sound* made by these two notes, whether sung, played on the piano or on another instrument, or seen on the page. Practice intervals by playing the first note and then singing or humming the second. Then check your pitch by playing the second note. Repeat this process in reverse, playing the top note and singing or humming the bottom.

Examples:

Above a given note: Below a given note:

Minor 3rd   Major 6th   Perfect 5th   Perfect 4th   Major 3rd   Minor 3rd

MELODY PLAYBACK

In order to memorize (by ear) and play back more confidently a melody that is played twice for you, listen the *first* time and try to determine:

1) the starting note (always one of the three notes of the tonic triad);
2) the general direction(s) of the notes;
3) the pattern(s) the notes form (e.g., broken triads, intervals, patterns by step, repeated notes, etc.); and,
4) the overall rhythmic design.

On the *second* listening, it will then be easier to play back the same melody from memory, without having seen the music.

Example:

①   the chord is played to establish the tonality
②   the starting note
③   the direction of the notes
④   intervals
⑤   the rhythmic design:
⑥   a major triad

MUSICAL ELEMENTS AND PATTERNS IN THIS VOLUME

Study these examples at the lesson.

1) a canon (p. 9)

2) an ascending G major scale between the hands (p. 9)

3) repeated notes (p. 10)

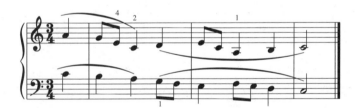

4) Alberti bass (p. 12)

5) various articulations (touches) and accents (p. 13)

6) contrary and similar (parallel) motion between the hands (p. 16)

7) a descending C major scale in the LH (p. 17)

8) chords built on a repeated Middle C in the LH (p. 20)

9) ornament patterns (turn) (p. 20)

10) intervals of a 6th in similar (parallel) motion between the hands (p. 21)

11) broken triads (p. 22)

12) a contrary motion melodic pattern with an imitative rhythmic pattern (p. 24)

13) repeated LH thirds and solid (blocked) triads formed from notes in both hands (p. 24)

14) syncopation in the RH melody (p. 26)

15) changing clefs (p. 28)

16) LH notes moving under the repeated eighth note A (p. 30)

17) a broken chord accompaniment (p. 32)

18) tied notes (p. 33)

19) a solid (blocked) triad accompaniment (p. 34)

20) a melody moving from hand to hand (p. 36)

21) a RH sequence (p. 36)

22) different articulations (touches) in each hand (p. 37)

23) a LH sequence (p. 40)

24) a LH melody moving under a repeated Middle C (p. 44)

DAILY SIGHT-READING EXERCISES No. 1

Directions to the student: Complete one set of sight-reading exercises and one daily rhythm (p. 10) at each practice session.

---

1 | FIRST DAY _May 19_ (date)

Name the key of this piece. (Answer: _____)

A. Köhl

---

2 | SECOND DAY _May 19_ (date)

The first four measures of the LH form the first four notes of what major scale? (Answer: _____)

T. Dunhill

Source: "Melody in C" from *First Year Pieces*

3

THIRD DAY _____ (*date*)

Notice the canon created between the hands. (See No. 1, p. 6)

F. Spindler

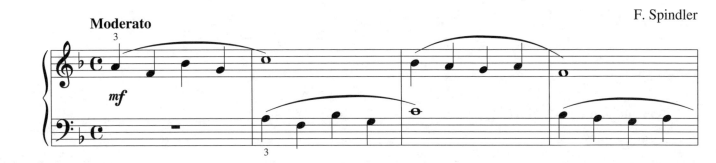

4

FOURTH DAY _____ (*date*)

Can you find the ascending scale divided between the hands?
Name this scale. (Answer: _____) (See No. 2, p. 6)

A. Markow

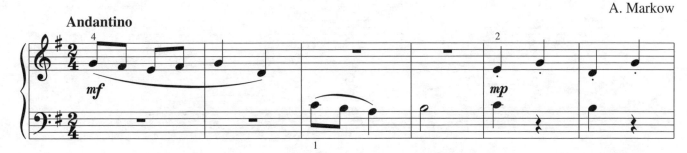

5   FIFTH DAY _____ (*date*)

a) In which clef is the LH written? (Answer: _____) Circle each set of two repeated notes.
   (See No. 3, p. 6)

C. Czerny

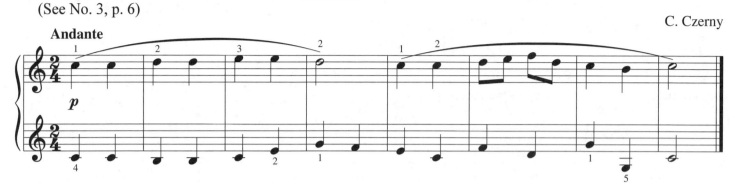

b) Circle all the intervals of a 3rd.

D.G. Türk

DAILY RHYTHMS FOR SIGHT READING NO. 1

Clap or tap the rhythm of the melodies. Maintain a steady pace and strong rhythmic (metrical) accentuation.

Play this triad in solid (blocked) form, then in **broken form**, beginning with the lowest note.

Play this turn.

Written   *Played*

Play this triad in broken form as shown, then in **solid (blocked) form**, striking all the notes together.

DAILY EAR-TRAINING EXERCISES No. 1

Directions to the student: Complete these ear-training exercises at home.

RHYTHM

Sing, clap, or tap the rhythm of these short melodies: (a) by looking at the music and (b) from memory.

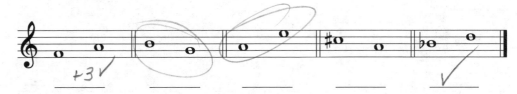

INTERVALS

Play the first note of each interval, then sing or hum the second. Repeat the process in reverse. Identify the interval and write its name underneath.

MELODY PLAYBACK

Name the key of each of the following melodies. For each example, play the tonic chord ONCE. Play the melody TWICE, observing the DIRECTIONS of the notes and the PATTERNS they form. Then play the melody from memory.

DAILY SIGHT-READING EXERCISES NO. 2

Directions to the student: Complete one set of sight-reading exercises and one daily rhythm (p. 14) at each practice session.

---

1 FIRST DAY _May 26/09_ *(date)*

What triad do the notes form in mm. 1, 3, and 5 of the LH Alberti bass? (Answer: _____) (See No. 4, p. 6)

F. Le Couppey

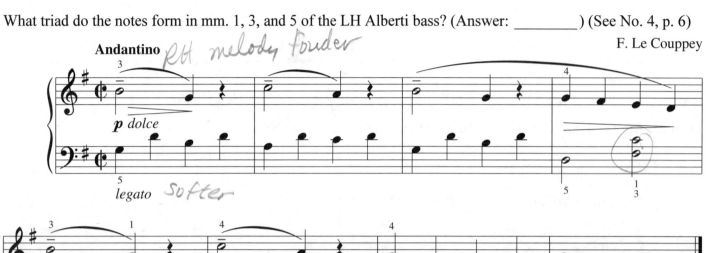

---

2 SECOND DAY _____ *(date)*

Which two measures in the LH are exactly the same? (Answer: _____)

F.J. Haydn

There are two broken triads in this piece. Circle them.

J.H. Buttstedt

3 THIRD DAY _June 8/09_ *(date)*

What is the relationship between the hands in this piece? (Answer: _____) Notice the various
articulations (touches) and the accents. (See No. 5, p. 6)

F. Swinstead

Source: "Follow My Leader" from *Work and Play*
© Copyright 1935 by The Associated Board of the Royal Schools of Music. Reprinted by permission.

4 FOURTH DAY _May 26/09_ *(date)*

Notice how the two four-measure phrases in the LH are exactly the same.

G.P. Telemann

5 FIFTH DAY _____ (date)

What chord do the notes in the LH form in mm. 2, 4, and 6? (Answer: _____)
Bracket mm. 2 and 3 in the LH. Which other two measures are identical? (Answer: _____)

C. Czerny

January 5/10

DAILY RHYTHMS FOR SIGHT READING NO. 2

Clap or tap the rhythm of the melodies. Maintain a steady pace and strong rhythmic (metrical) accentuation.

FIRST DAY

SECOND DAY

THIRD DAY

FOURTH DAY

FIFTH DAY

Play this triad in broken form as shown, then in **solid (blocked) form**, striking all the notes together.

Play this turn.

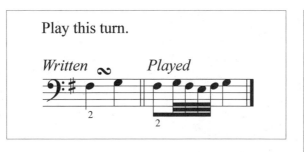

Play this triad in solid (blocked) form, then in **broken form**, beginning with the lowest note.

Daily Ear-Training Exercises No. 2

Directions to the student: Complete these ear-training exercises at home.

RHYTHM

Sing, clap, or tap the rhythm of these short melodies: (a) by looking at the music and (b) from memory.

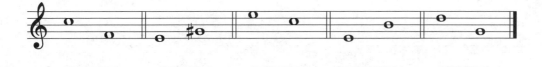

INTERVALS

Play the first note of each interval, then sing or hum the second. Repeat the process in reverse. Identify the interval and write its name underneath.

_____   _____   _____   _____   _____

MELODY PLAYBACK

Name the key of each of the following melodies. For each example, play the tonic chord ONCE. Play the melody TWICE, observing the DIRECTIONS of the notes and the PATTERNS they form. Then play the melody from memory.

DAILY SIGHT-READING EXERCISES No. 3

Directions to the student: Complete one set of sight-reading exercises and one daily rhythm (p. 18) at each practice session.

1 FIRST DAY _____ (date)

See how mm. 1 and 5 move in contrary motion, and mm. 2 and 6 move in similar (parallel) motion. (See No. 6, p. 6)

J. Hook

2 SECOND DAY _Junt 23_ (date)

In which measures is the rhythm (𝅘𝅥𝅭 𝅘𝅥𝅮𝅘𝅥𝅮 | 𝅗𝅥) found? (Answer: _____) Count and clap this rhythm.

H. Purcell

3   THIRD DAY   *June 8/09*   (*date*)

Circle all the intervals of a 4th.

M. Kymlicka

Source: "Kites" from *Simple Music for Piano*, Book 1
Used by permission of the composer.

---

4   FOURTH DAY _____ (*date*)

a) Circle the repeated notes in the RH.

H. Purcell

b) Circle the notes that form the complete C major descending scale in the LH. (See No. 7, p. 6)

arr. H. Willan

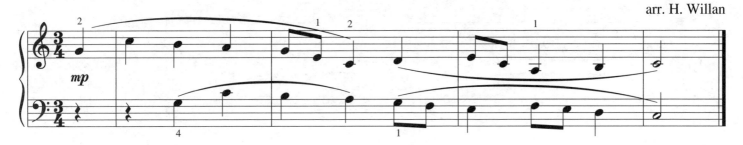

Source: "Pretty Polly Oliver" from *Songs of the British Isles*, Volume 2
Used by permission of Waterloo Music Co., Ltd.

5 FIFTH DAY _____ (*date*)

Do all the eighth notes in this piece fit into a five-finger position? (Answer: ___)

Happily

L. Niamath

Source: "Swinging" from *In My Garden*

DAILY RHYTHMS FOR SIGHT READING NO. 3

Clap or tap the rhythm of the melodies. Maintain a steady pace and strong rhythmic (metrical) accentuation.

FIRST DAY

SECOND DAY

THIRD DAY

FOURTH DAY

FIFTH DAY

Play this triad in solid (blocked) form, then in **broken form**, beginning with the lowest note.

Play the following turns.

Play this triad in broken form as shown, then in **solid (blocked) form,** striking all the notes together.

Daily Ear Training Exercises No. 3

Directions to the student: Complete these ear-training exercises at home.

RHYTHM

Sing, clap, or tap the rhythm of these short melodies: (a) by looking at the music and (b) from memory.

INTERVALS

Play the first note of each interval, then sing or hum the second. Repeat the process in reverse. Identify the interval and write its name underneath.

MELODY PLAYBACK

Name the key of each of the following melodies. For each example, play the tonic chord ONCE. Play the melody TWICE, observing the DIRECTIONS of the notes and the PATTERNS they form. Then play the melody from memory.

DAILY SIGHT-READING EXERCISES NO. 4

Directions to the student: Complete one set of sight-reading exercises and one daily rhythm (p. 22) at each practice session.

1

FIRST DAY _____ (*date*)

Can you see that the first five LH chords are built up from Middle C? (See No. 8, p. 6)

T.F. Dunhill

Source: "The Old Abbey" from *First Year Pieces*
© Copyright 1935 by The Associated Board of the Royal Schools of Music. Reprinted by permission.

2

SECOND DAY _____ (*date*)

What ornament can you find written out in m. 2 of the RH? (Answer: _____) (See No. 9, p. 6)

C. Graupner

3 THIRD DAY _____ (*date*)

See how the notes move under the repeated Middle C in the LH. Circle these notes.

T.F. Dunhill

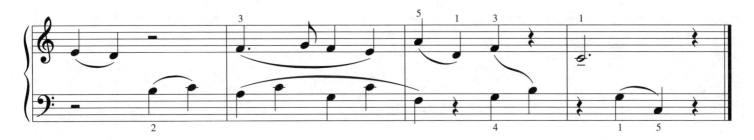

Source: "A Sad Story" from *First Year Pieces*
© Copyright 1935 by The Associated Board of the Royal Schools of Music. Reprinted by permission.

4 FOURTH DAY _____ (*date*)

Notice how the first three notes in mm. 5 and 6 move in similar (parallel) motion by the interval of a 6th.
(See No. 10, p. 6)

L. London

5   FIFTH DAY _____ (*date*)

Circle all the broken triads. (See No. 11, p. 6)

N.J. Hüllmandel

DAILY RHYTHMS FOR SIGHT READING NO. 4

Clap or tap the rhythm of the melodies. Maintain a steady pace and strong rhythmic (metrical) accentuation.

FIRST DAY

SECOND DAY

THIRD DAY

FOURTH DAY

FIFTH DAY

Play this triad in broken form, as shown, then in **solid (blocked) form**, striking all the notes together.

Play this mordent.

Written   *Played*

Play this triad in solid (blocked) form, then in **broken form,** beginning with the middle note.

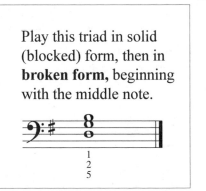

DAILY EAR-TRAINING EXERCISES NO. 4

Directions to the student: Complete these ear-training exercises at home.

RHYTHM

Sing, clap, or tap the rhythm of these short melodies: (a) by looking at the music and (b) from memory.

INTERVALS

Play the first note of each interval, then sing or hum the second. Repeat the process in reverse. Identify the interval and write its name underneath.

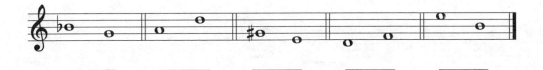

MELODY PLAYBACK

Name the key of each of the following melodies. For each example, play the tonic chord ONCE. Play the melody TWICE, observing the DIRECTIONS of the notes and the PATTERNS they form. Then play the melody from memory.

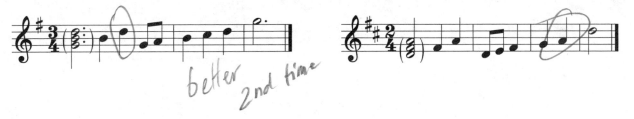

DAILY SIGHT-READING EXERCISES No. 5

Directions to the student: Complete one set of sight-reading exercises and one daily rhythm (p. 26) at each practice session.

1   FIRST DAY ___June 23/09___ *(date)*

Bracket the imitative rhythmic patterns between the hands .
(See No. 12, p. 6)

C. Elliot

Source: "Nine Canons for Grade One" from *17 Canons*
Used by permission of the Waterloo Music Co., Ltd.

2   SECOND DAY _____ *(date)*

Circle the repeated 3rds in the LH. (See No. 13, p. 7)

L. Mozart

3 THIRD DAY _____ (*date*)

Identify the descending scale in the LH. (Answer: _____)

R. Cento

Source: "Practicing My Piano" from *Sandcastles*

4 FOURTH DAY _____ (*date*)

Bracket the measures in which the LH imitates the RH.

D.G. Türk

5   FIFTH DAY _____ (date)

What note is repeated on the second and fourth quarter notes (♩) of each measure in the LH? (Answer: _____)
Notice the syncopation in the RH melody. (See No. 14, p. 7)

I. Bartalus

DAILY RHYTHMS FOR SIGHT READING NO. 5

Clap or tap the rhythm of the melodies. Maintain a steady pace and strong rhythmic (metrical) accentuation.

FIRST DAY

SECOND DAY

THIRD DAY

FOURTH DAY

FIFTH DAY

Play the given note. Then, **without looking at the keyboard**, and still holding the note, play the two notes that complete the triad in *root position*.

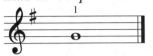

Play this short trill.

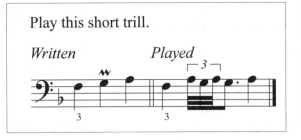

Play the given note. Then, **without looking at the keyboard**, and still holding the note, play the two notes that complete the triad in *first inversion*.

DAILY EAR TRAINING EXERCISES NO. 5

Directions to the student: Complete these ear-training exercises at home.

RHYTHM

Sing, clap, or tap the rhythm of these short melodies: (a) by looking at the music and (b) from memory.

INTERVALS

Play the first note of each interval, then sing or hum the second. Repeat the process in reverse. Identify the interval and write its name underneath.

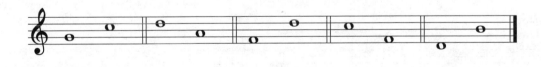

MELODY PLAYBACK

Name the key of each of the following melodies. For each example, play the tonic chord ONCE. Play the melody TWICE, observing the DIRECTIONS of the notes and the PATTERNS they form. Then play the melody from memory.

DAILY SIGHT-READING EXERCISES No. 6

Directions to the student: Complete one set of sight-reading exercises and one daily rhythm (p. 30) at each practice session.

1 FIRST DAY _____ (date)

Notice that the RH four-measure melody is repeated except for the last two notes, which are reversed.

2 SECOND DAY _____ (date)

Circle the changing clefs in the LH. (See No. 15, p. 7)

D.G. Türk

3 THIRD DAY _____ (*date*)

Circle the intervals of a broken or solid (blocked) 5th.

F. Le Couppey

4 FOURTH DAY _____ (*date*)

Circle the eighth notes forming the descending scale in the RH. Name this scale. (Answer: _____)

G.F. Handel

5   FIFTH DAY _____ *(date)*

Notice how the LH notes move under the repeated eighth note A. (See No. 16, p. 7)

arr. E. MacMillan
and B. Berlin

Source: *Italian Folk Song*
Used by permission of the Estate of E. MacMillan.

DAILY RHYTHMS FOR SIGHT READING No. 6

Clap or tap the rhythm of the melodies. Maintain a steady pace and strong rhythmic (metrical) accentuation.

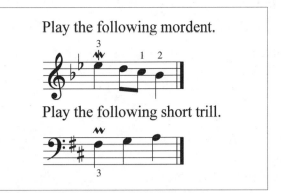

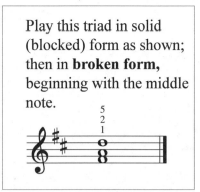

DAILY EAR-TRAINING EXERCISES NO. 6

Directions to the student: Complete these ear-training exercises at home.

RHYTHM

Sing, clap, or tap the rhythm of these short melodies: (a) by looking at the music and (b) from memory.

INTERVALS

Play the first note of each interval, then sing or hum the second. Repeat the process in reverse. Identify the interval and write its name underneath.

MELODY PLAYBACK

Name the key of each of the following melodies. For each example, play the tonic chord ONCE. Play the melody TWICE, observing the DIRECTIONS of the notes and the PATTERNS they form. Then play the melody from memory.

DAILY SIGHT-READING EXERCISES No. 7

Directions to the student: Complete one set of sight-reading exercises and one daily rhythm (p. 34) at each practice session.

---

1   FIRST DAY _____ (*date*)

Count all the broken tonic (I) triads in the LH. (Number: _____). (See No. 17, p. 7)

L. Kohler

---

2   SECOND DAY _____ (*date*)

What key is this piece in? (Answer: _____)

L. London

3 THIRD DAY _____ (*date*)

Circle the accidentals in this piece, then name them.

L. Eurina

Source: "Jazz Etude No. 1" from *Ukrainian Echoes*

4 FOURTH DAY _____ (*date*)

Mark the tied notes with an "X." (See No. 18, p. 7)

C. Gurlitt

5 FIFTH DAY _____ (date)

Circle all the second inversion LH triads. (See No. 19, p. 7)

R. Bruce

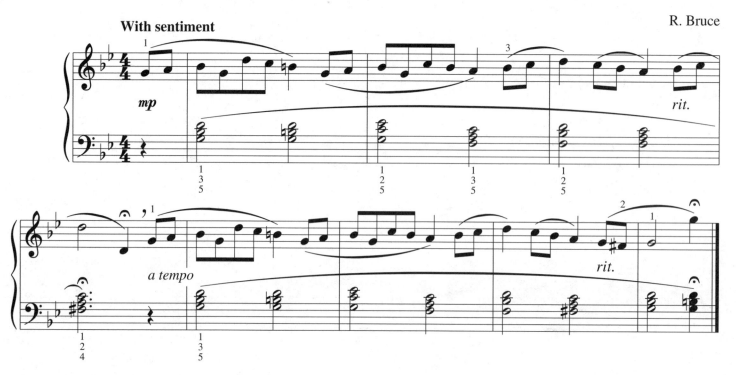

Source: "Old Photographs" from *24 Easy Pieces*
Used by permission of the composer.

DAILY RHYTHMS FOR SIGHT READING NO. 7

Clap or tap the rhythm of the melodies. Maintain a steady pace and strong rhythmic (metrical) accentuation.

Play the given note. Then, **without looking at the keyboard,** and still holding the note, play the two notes that complete the triad in *first inversion.*

Play this structured (rhythmic) trill beginning on the principal note.

Written   *Played*

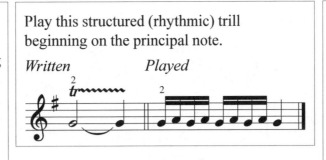

Play the given note. Then, **without looking at the keyboard,** and still holding the note, play the two notes that complete the triad in *second inversion.*

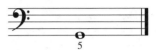

DAILY EAR-TRAINING EXERCISES NO. 7

Directions to the student: Complete these ear-training exercises at home.

RHYTHM

Sing, clap, or tap the rhythm of these short melodies: (a) by looking at the music and (b) from memory.

INTERVALS

Play the first note of each interval, then sing or hum the second. Repeat the process in reverse. Identify the interval and write its name underneath.

_____   _____   _____   _____   _____

MELODY PLAYBACK

Name the key of each of the following melodies. For each example, play the tonic chord ONCE. Play the melody TWICE, observing the DIRECTIONS of the notes and the PATTERNS they form. Then play the melody from memory.

DAILY SIGHT-READING EXERCISES NO. 8

Directions to the student: Complete one set of sight-reading exercises and one daily rhythm (p. 38) at each practice session.

---

1   FIRST DAY _____ (date)

Notice how the melody moves from one hand to the other. (See No. 20, p. 7)

E. Breslaur

---

2   SECOND DAY _____ (date)

Can you find the four descending sequences? Circle the first note of each one. (See No. 21, p. 7)

G.F. Handel

3   THIRD DAY _____ (*date*)

Clap the rhythmic pattern (♩ ♪♪ ♪). How many of these patterns are there in this piece? (Answer: _____)

T.F. Dunhill

Source: "A Little Hush-Song" from *First Year Pieces*
© Copyright 1935 by The Associated Board of the Royal Schools of Music. Reprinted by permission.

4   FOURTH DAY _____ (*date*)

Notice the legato in the RH and the staccato in the LH. (See No. 22, p. 7)

C. Franck

5   FIFTH DAY _____ *(date)*

Circle all the intervals of a 4th.

G. Kirchhoff

DAILY RHYTHMS FOR SIGHT READING NO. 8

Clap or tap the rhythm of the melodies. Maintain a steady pace and strong rhythmic (metrical) accentuation.

FIRST DAY

SECOND DAY

THIRD DAY

FOURTH DAY

FIFTH DAY

Play this triad in solid (blocked) form, then in **broken form** beginning with the highest note.

Play this structured (rhythmic) trill beginning on the upper note.

Written   *Played*

Play this triad in broken form as shown, then in **solid (blocked) form,** striking all the notes together.

DAILY EAR-TRAINING EXERCISES NO. 8

Directions to the student: Complete these ear-training exercises at home.

RHYTHM

Sing, clap, or tap the rhythm of these short melodies: (a) by looking at the music and (b) from memory.

INTERVALS

Play the first note of each interval, then sing or hum the second. Repeat the process in reverse. Identify the interval and write its name underneath.

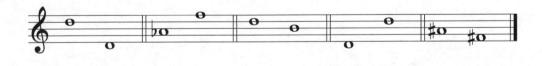

MELODY PLAYBACK

Name the key of each of the following melodies. For each example, play the tonic chord ONCE. Play the melody TWICE, observing the DIRECTIONS of the notes and the PATTERNS they form. Then play the melody from memory.

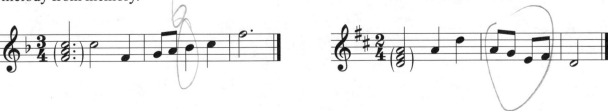

DAILY SIGHT-READING EXERCISES NO. 9

Directions to the student: Complete one set of sight-reading exercises and one daily rhythm (p. 42) at each practice session.

Circle the notes on the first and third beats of each measure in the LH. Now play them and hear the melody they form.

A. Biehl

Notice the sequence in the LH. Circle the first note of each group of the sequence. (See No. 23, p. 7)

G.F. Handel

3   THIRD DAY _____ (*date*)

Notice the canon between the hands.

C. Elliot

Source: "Nine Canons for Grade One" from *17 Canons*
Used by permission of the Waterloo Music Co., Ltd.

---

4   FOURTH DAY _____ (*date*)

Clap the dotted rhythm in the RH (♪. ♫ ♩ ♪│♩. ♩.).

arr. E. MacMillan
and B. Berlin

Source: *Musette*
Used by permission of the Estate of E. MacMillan.

5   FIFTH DAY _____ (*date*)

Clap the rhythmic patterns in the LH (♪. ♪ | ♪ ♪ | ♩ and ♪♪♪♪ | ♩ ♩).

R. Bruce

Brightly

Source: "Trumpets" from *24 Easy Pieces*
Used by permission of the composer.

DAILY RHYTHMS FOR SIGHT READING NO. 9

Clap or tap the rhythm of the melodies. Maintain a steady pace and strong rhythmic (metrical) accentuation.

FIRST DAY

SECOND DAY

THIRD DAY

FOURTH DAY

FIFTH DAY

Play the given note. Then, **without looking at the keyboard**, and still holding the note, play the two notes that complete the triad in second *inversion*.

Play the following trills:
(a) beginning on the upper note.
(b) beginning on the principal note.

Play the given note. Then, **without looking at the keyboard**, and still holding the note, play the two notes that complete the triad in *root position*.

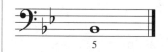

Daily Ear-Training Exercises No. 9

Directions to the student: Complete these ear-training exercises at home.

RHYTHM

Sing, clap, or tap the rhythm of these short melodies: (a) by looking at the music and (b) from memory.

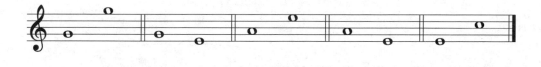

INTERVALS

Play the first note of each interval, then sing or hum the second. Repeat the process in reverse. Identify the interval and write its name underneath.

MELODY PLAYBACK

Name the key of each of the following melodies. For each example, play the tonic chord ONCE. Play the melody TWICE, observing the DIRECTIONS of the notes and the PATTERNS they form. Then play the melody from memory.

DAILY SIGHT-READING EXERCISES No. 10

Directions to the student: Complete one set of sight-reading exercises and one daily rhythm (p. 46) at each practice session.

1   FIRST DAY _____ (*date*)

a) Circle the repeated notes in each hand.

T. Attwood

b) Circle the intervals of a 3rd.

D.G. Türk

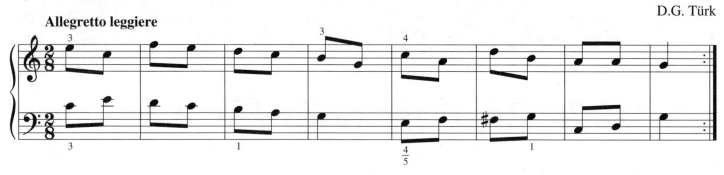

2   SECOND DAY _____ (*date*)

a) Notice the LH melody moving under the repeated Middle C. (See No. 24, p. 7)

C. Reinecke

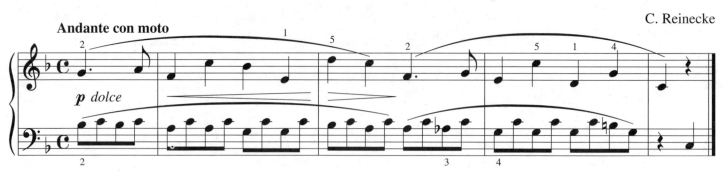

b) Notice the $\frac{2}{2}$ time signature. Can you name the key of this piece? (Answer: _____)

J.P. Kirnberger

3 THIRD DAY _____ (*date*)

Circle the changing clefs in the LH.

T. Kirchner

4 FOURTH DAY _____ (*date*)

Be sure to observe the accidentals when you play this piece.

H. Purcell

5

FIFTH DAY _____ (*date*)

Mark with an "X" the intervals of a 7th and an octave in the LH.

J.P. Rameau

DAILY RHYTHMS FOR SIGHT READING No. 10

Clap or tap the rhythm of the melodies. Maintain a steady pace and strong rhythmic (metrical) accentuation.

Play this triad in broken form as shown, then in **solid (blocked) form,** striking all the notes together.

Play the following ornaments.

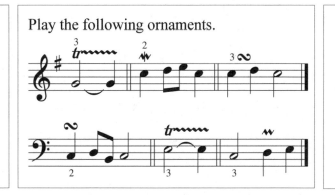

Play this triad in solid (blocked) form, then in **broken form** beginning with the highest note.

DAILY EAR-TRAINING EXERCISES No. 10

Directions to the student: Complete these ear-training exercises at home.

RHYTHM

Sing, clap, or tap the rhythm of these short melodies: (a) by looking at the music and (b) from memory.

INTERVALS

Play the first note of each interval, then sing or hum the second. Repeat the process in reverse. Identify the interval and write its name underneath.

_____   _____   _____   _____

MELODY PLAYBACK

Name the key of each of the following melodies. For each example, play the tonic chord ONCE. Play the melody TWICE, observing the DIRECTIONS of the notes and the PATTERNS they form. Then play the melody from memory.

★ FOUR STAR TEST No. 1 ★

GIVEN BY THE TEACHER AT THE LESSON

SIGHT-READING TEST

Teacher's grading

J. Hook

E. Breslaur

Clap or tap the rhythm of the following melody.

EAR TEST

For this test, the teacher will select from the examples found on pp. 59–61:
    1) a rhythm for clapping, tapping, or singing,
    2) a number of intervals for singing or identifying,
    3) a melody for playback.

Instructions on how to administer the three segments of the Ear Tests are also found on these pages.
For additional material, see the series *Melody Playback/Singback* and *Rhythm Clapback/Singback.*

★ FOUR STAR TEST NO. 2 ★

GIVEN BY THE TEACHER AT THE LESSON

SIGHT-READING TEST

Teacher's grading

C. Loeschhorn

E. Breslaur

Clap or tap the rhythm of the following melody.

EAR TEST

For this test, the teacher will select from the examples found on pp. 59–61:

1) a rhythm for clapping, tapping, or singing,
2) a number of intervals for singing or identifying,
3) a melody for playback.

Instructions on how to administer the three segments of the Ear Tests are also found on these pages.
For additional material, see the series *Melody Playback/Singback* and *Rhythm Clapback/Singback*.

★ FOUR STAR TEST No. 3 ★

GIVEN BY THE TEACHER AT THE LESSON

SIGHT-READING TEST

Teacher's grading

Clap or tap the rhythm of the following melody.

EAR TEST

For this test, the teacher will select from the examples found on pp. 59–61:

1) a rhythm for clapping, tapping, or singing,
2) a number of intervals for singing or identifying,
3) a melody for playback.

Instructions on how to administer the three segments of the Ear Tests are also found on these pages.
For additional material, see the series *Melody Playback/Singback* and *Rhythm Clapback/Singback.*

★ FOUR STAR TEST NO. 4 ★

GIVEN BY THE TEACHER AT THE LESSON

SIGHT-READING TEST

Teacher's grading

Clap or tap the rhythm of the following melody.

EAR TEST

For this test, the teacher will select from the examples found on pp. 59–61:

1) a rhythm for clapping, tapping, or singing,
2) a number of intervals for singing or identifying,
3) a melody for playback.

Instructions on how to administer the three segments of the Ear Tests are also found on these pages.
For additional material, see the series *Melody Playback/Singback* and *Rhythm Clapback/Singback*.

★ FOUR STAR TEST NO. 5 ★

GIVEN BY THE TEACHER AT THE LESSON

SIGHT-READING TEST

Teacher's grading

Clap or tap the rhythm of the following melody.

EAR TEST

For this test, the teacher will select from the examples found on pp. 59–61:
1) a rhythm for clapping, tapping, or singing,
2) a number of intervals for singing or identifying,
3) a melody for playback.

Instructions on how to administer the three segments of the Ear Tests are also found on these pages.
For additional material, see the series *Melody Playback/Singback* and *Rhythm Clapback/Singback.*

FOUR STAR TEST NO. 6

GIVEN BY THE TEACHER AT THE LESSON

SIGHT-READING TEST

Teacher's grading

D.G. Türk

M. Clementi

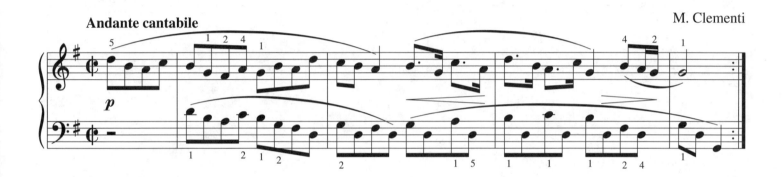

Clap or tap the rhythm of the following melody.

EAR TEST

For this test, the teacher will select from the examples found on pp. 59–61:

1) a rhythm for clapping, tapping, or singing,
2) a number of intervals for singing or identifying,
3) a melody for playback.

Instructions on how to administer the three segments of the Ear Tests are also found on these pages.
For additional material, see the series *Melody Playback/Singback* and *Rhythm Clapback/Singback.*

★ FOUR STAR TEST NO. 7 ★

GIVEN BY THE TEACHER AT THE LESSON

SIGHT-READING TEST

Teacher's grading

Clap or tap the rhythm of the following melody.

EAR TEST

For this test, the teacher will select from the examples found on pp. 59–61:
1) a rhythm for clapping, tapping, or singing,
2) a number of intervals for singing or identifying,
3) a melody for playback.

Instructions on how to administer the three segments of the Ear Tests are also found on these pages.
For additional material, see the series *Melody Playback/Singback* and *Rhythm Clapback/Singback*.

FOUR STAR TEST No. 8

GIVEN BY THE TEACHER AT THE LESSON

SIGHT-READING TEST

Teacher's grading

G.F. Handel

C. Gurlitt

Clap or tap the rhythm of the following melody.

EAR TEST

For this test, the teacher will select from the examples found on pp. 59–61:

1) a rhythm for clapping, tapping, or singing,
2) a number of intervals for singing or identifying,
3) a melody for playback.

Instructions on how to administer the three segments of the Ear Tests are also found on these pages.
For additional material, see the series *Melody Playback/Singback* and *Rhythm Clapback/Singback*.

★ FOUR STAR TEST NO. 9 ★

GIVEN BY THE TEACHER AT THE LESSON

SIGHT-READING TEST

Teacher's grading

Clap or tap the rhythm of the following melody.

EAR TEST

For this test, the teacher will select from the examples found on pp. 59–61:
1) a rhythm for clapping, tapping, or singing,
2) a number of intervals for singing or identifying,
3) a melody for playback.

Instructions on how to administer the three segments of the Ear Tests are also found on these pages.
For additional material, see the series *Melody Playback/Singback* and *Rhythm Clapback/Singback.*

★ FOUR STAR TEST NO. 10 ★

GIVEN BY THE TEACHER AT THE LESSON

SIGHT-READING TEST

Teacher's grading

H. Purcell

C. Gurlitt

Clap or tap the rhythm of the following melody.

Ap-27

EAR TEST

For this test, the teacher will select from the examples found on pp. 59–61:

1) a rhythm for clapping, tapping, or singing,
2) a number of intervals for singing or identifying,
3) a melody for playback.

Instructions on how to administer the three segments of the Ear Tests are also found on these pages.
For additional material, see the series *Melody Playback/Singback* and *Rhythm Clapback/Singback.*

★ FINAL FOUR STAR TEST ★

This test will be given before filling in and signing the Certificate of Achievement.

SIGHT-READING TEST

Teacher's grading

D.G. Türk

C.M. von Weber

Clap or tap the rhythm of the following melody.

EAR TEST

For this test, the teacher will select from the examples found on pp. 59–61:

1) a rhythm for clapping, tapping, or singing,
2) a number of intervals for singing or identifying,
3) a melody for playback.

Instructions on how to administer the three segments of the Ear Tests are also found on these pages.
For additional material, see the series *Melody Playback/Singback* and *Rhythm Clapback/Singback*.

EAR TESTS

GIVEN BY THE TEACHER AT THE LESSON

During these tests, the student must not see the keyboard or look at the music.

1) RHYTHM

The teacher selects one of the following short melodies and plays it TWICE.
The student then sings, claps, or taps the rhythm of the short melody from memory.

2) INTERVALS

The teacher selects and names one of the following interval, and plays the first note ONCE. The student sings or hums the other note; OR

The teacher plays the interval in broken form ONCE and the student *identifies* (names) it by ear. The teacher then repeats this procedure with several other intervals.

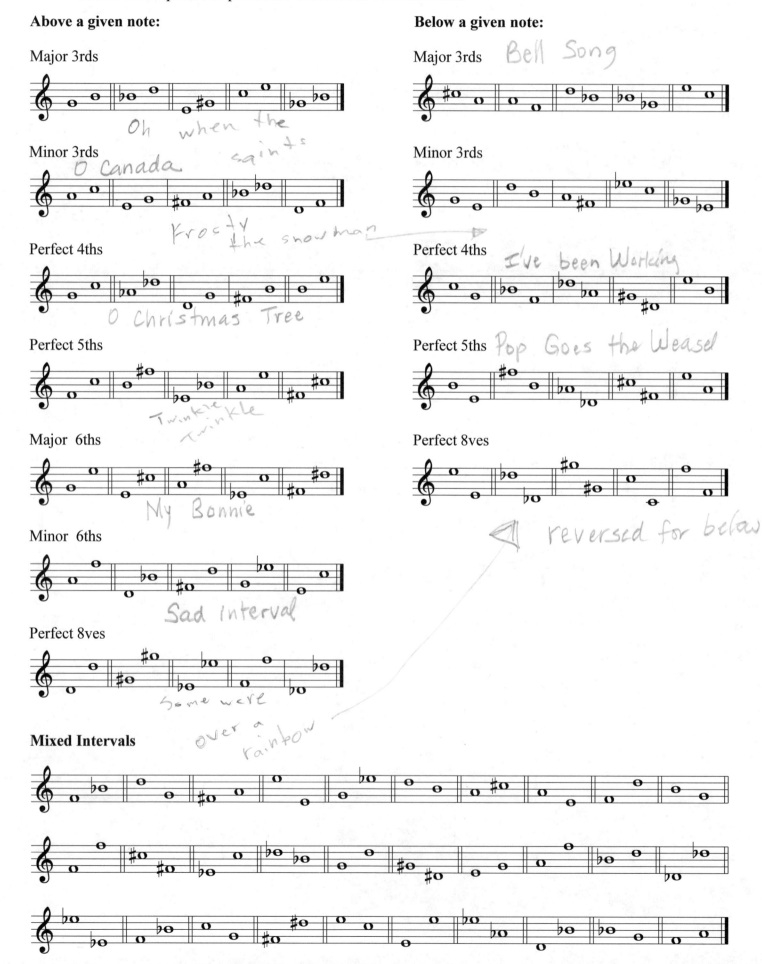

61

3) MELODY PLAYBACK

The teacher selects one of the following melodies, names the key, plays the tonic chord ONCE, and then plays the melody TWICE. The student then plays back the melody from memory.

Supplementary Material

Teachers may test students at the lesson by choosing one example from each of the **Chords** and **18th-century Ornament** categories. The **Melody Writing** exercises should be assigned for home practice.

1) CHORDS

Play the given note. Then, **without looking at the keyboard**, and still holding the note, play the two notes that complete the major triad in *root position*.

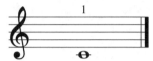

Play the given note. Then, **without looking at the keyboard**, and still holding the note, play the two notes that complete the major triad in *first inversion*.

Play the given note. Then, **without looking at the keyboard**, and still holding the note, play the two notes that complete the major triad in *second inversion*.

Play the given note. Then, **without looking at the keyboard**, and still holding the note, play the two notes that complete the minor triad in *root position*.

Play the given note. Then, **without looking at the keyboard**, and still holding the note, play the two notes that complete the minor triad in *first inversion*.

Play the given note. Then, **without looking at the keyboard**, and still holding the note, play the two notes that complete the minor triad in *second inversion*.

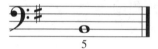

Play this triad in solid (blocked) form, then in **broken form**, beginning with the lowest note.

Play this triad in solid (blocked) form, then in **broken form**, beginning with the middle note.

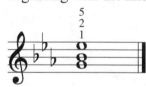

Play this triad in solid (blocked) form, then in **broken form**, beginning with the highest note.

Play this triad in solid (blocked) form, then in **broken form**, beginning with the lowest note.

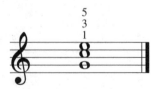

Play this triad in solid (blocked) form, then in **broken form**, beginning with the middle note.

Play this triad in solid (blocked) form, then in **broken form**, beginning with the highest note.

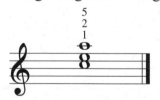

Play this triad in broken form as shown, then in **solid form,** striking all the notes together.

Play this triad in broken form as shown, then in **solid form,** striking all the notes together.

Play this triad in broken form as shown, then in **solid form,** striking all the notes together.

Play this triad in broken form as shown, then in **solid form,** striking all the notes together.

Play this triad in broken form as shown, then in **solid form,** striking all the notes together.

Play this triad in broken form as shown, then in **solid form,** striking all the notes together.

Play this triad in broken form as shown, then in **solid form,** striking all the notes together.

2) 18TH-CENTURY ORNAMENTS

Name and play the following ornaments.

3) MELODY WRITING

Complete each of the following melodies by adding notes as directed. Then play the melody: (a) by looking at the music and (b) from memory.

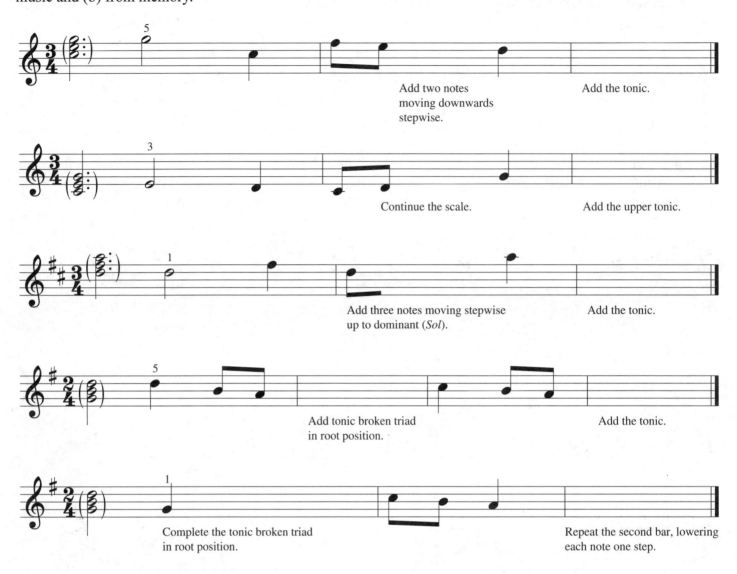

Add two notes moving downwards stepwise.

Add the tonic.

Continue the scale.

Add the upper tonic.

Add three notes moving stepwise up to dominant (*Sol*).

Add the tonic.

Add tonic broken triad in root position.

Add the tonic.

Complete the tonic broken triad in root position.

Repeat the second bar, lowering each note one step.

Complete each of the following melodies by adding notes of your choice. Then play the melody: (a) by looking at the music and (b) from memory.